CW00945965

Spelling

How to use this book with your child:

It is recommended that an adult spends time with a child while doing any kind of school practice, to offer encouragement and guidance. Find a quiet place to work, preferably at a table, and encourage your child to hold his or her pen or pencil correctly.

Try to work at your child's pace and avoid spending too long on any one page or activity. Most of all, emphasise the fun element of what you are doing and enjoy this special and exciting time!

Don't forget to add your reward sticker to each page you complete!

Reward
sticker!

Designed by Plum5
Illustrations by Sue King, Sharon Smart and Andy Geeson
Educational consultant Chris Andrew

Autumn
Publishing

CVC words (consonant vowel consonant)

All of the words below have a vowel missing.
Write in the missing letters.

c__t   b__d

f__n   c__w   d__g

h__n   n__t

Reward
sticker!

Which vowels are missing?

Write in the correct vowels to complete the words.

k__ng

fl___g

b___rd

fr___g

dr___m

sh__p

h___rp

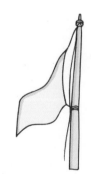

m___st

sw__m

'ch', 'sh', 'th' and 'wh' words

Look at the words in the boxes and colour any that have a **ch** sound blue, a **sh** sound red, a **th** sound green and a **wh** sound yellow.

shell	moth	chop
thin	chip	wish
when	with	fish

Now, using the sounds below, complete the words. Some sounds will go at the start of the word, some at the end. Watch out - you may be able to use more than one sound for some words!

ch	sh	th	wh

____ape   wa____   ____urch

wi____   mu____   ____ich

Reward sticker!

Ending in 'll', 'ss', 'ff', 'zz' and 'ck'

Using the sounds in the boxes below complete the words. There may be more than one sound that works!

| ll | ss | ff | zz | ck |

she____   mo____   so____   du____

be____   bu____   fi____

Now look at the words in the boxes and colour any that have a **ss** sound blue, a **ll** sound red, a **zz** sound green, a **ck** purple and an **ff** sound yellow.

ball	fizz	shall
block	muck	moss
pass	buzz	fluff

Reward sticker!

5

Thinking of fishing

Look at the words in the boxes and shade any that have an **ng** sound blue and an **nk** sound red. Look out, some don't have either!

link	thing	plank
sing	sprinkle	clunk
wand	croak	along

Now look at the picture. Which line does not lead to a word that ends in **ng** or **nk?** Write your answer in the box.

Reward sticker!

Words ending in 'tch' and 've'

Look at the words below. Some of them have the **tch** sound and the others have the **ve** sound. Draw a line from each word to the correct sound.

live

hatch

catch

stopwatch

glove

witch

hive

tch	ve

Reward sticker!

Words ending in 's' and 'es'

The words below are **plurals**. That means there is more than one of each thing. Colour in the words that end in **es** blue and say them out loud. What do you notice about them?
They have an extra beat to the word – try clapping it out.
e.g. dog**s** = 1 clap   match**es** = 2 claps

cats	witches
thanks	catches
foxes	bags
spends	matches
rocks	boxes
hatches	balls
lamps	dogs

Reward sticker!

Comparisons

We add on the endings **er** or **est** to compare things.
For example: short – short**er** – short**est**.
Look at the words below. Can you add **er** or **est** on to these words?

	er	est
fast	fast____	fast_____
tall	tall____	tall_____
low	low____	low_____
kind	_____	_____
grand	_____	_____

Can you think of some of your own?

_____ _____   _____

_____ _____   _____

Words ending in 'er' and 'est'

Look at the words in the boxes and choose one for each of the endings below. Which words can be used with both **er** and **est**? Colour them in red.

slow

quick

hunt

buzz

show

low

play

old

strong

hard

flow

spray

_____er   _____est

_____er   _____est

_____er   _____est

_____er   _____est

_____er   _____est

_____er   _____est

Reward sticker!

Words ending in 'ay' and 'oy'

Can you think of some words that end in **ay**? Write them below.

___ay   ___ay   ___ay   ___ay

Now think of some words that end in **oy**. Write them below.

___oy   ___oy   ___oy   ___oy

See how many **ay** and **oy** words you can find in this word search.
five is good, eight is excellent, over 10 is magnificent!

c	l	s	p	x	v	g	t	f
s	a	t	y	p	m	e	f	t
t	y	r	a	v	a	t	x	o
a	l	a	w	k	y	r	m	y
y	z	y	z	w	f	a	a	g
s	t	b	y	h	k	y	f	s
u	y	c	o	y	s	b	h	j
h	z	a	b	j	o	y	n	e
t	e	b	d	h	w	t	n	v

Reward
sticker!

11

You're the teacher!

Some words have an **ay** sound in them that looks like **ai**.
Look at the words below and circle the spellings that are correct.

rain   wayt   trayn
rayn   wait   train

afraid   fayl   tail
afrayd   fail   tayl

Some words have an **oy** sound in them that looks like **oi**.
Look at the words below and circle the spellings that are incorrect.

oyl   spoil   joyn
oil   spoyl   join

point   soil   boyl
poynt   soyl   boil

Reward sticker!

Make a cake!

Some words have an **ay** sound but are actually written like this:

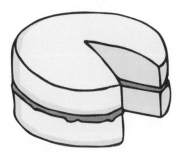

c<u>a</u>k<u>e</u>

consonant + **a** + consonant + **e**

You could call this letter sequence 'make a cake' to help you remember the spelling.

Try it with these words then match them to the pictures. Write out the words then draw a line from the correct word to the right picture.

cake   **lake**   **flame**   **game**

__a__e

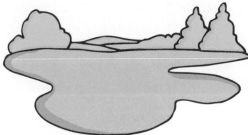

__a__e

__a__e

__ __a__e

Reward sticker!

Five alive

You could call this 'five alive' because the spelling pattern is

f<u>i</u>v<u>e</u>   consonant + **i** + consonant + **e**

Find as many **i_e** words as you can in the word search.

five	time	nine
ride	side	life
like	line	
hike	hide	

x	n	y	l	i	k	e	m	x	x
h	i	j	g	r	d	k	j	s	t
p	n	b	l	i	s	a	h	e	i
a	e	m	i	d	i	c	i	o	m
l	y	f	n	e	d	w	d	h	e
i	l	i	e	s	t	r	e	t	h
f	i	v	d	s	i	d	e	u	e
e	k	e	a	m	r	s	w	d	k
l	i	n	m	h	i	k	e	b	i
x	q	m	y	x	y	b	o	i	k

Reward
sticker!

Spelling patterns

Can you spot the spelling pattern in the words below?

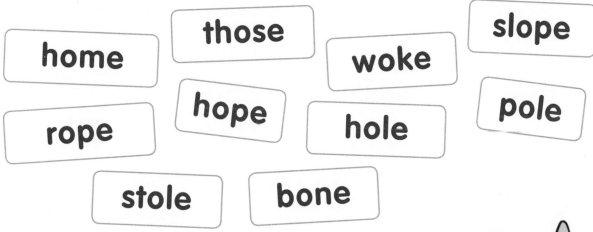

home · those · woke · slope · hope · hole · pole · rope · stole · bone

That's right the vowels go **o** then **e**.

Can you write a silly sentence that uses lots of these words?

e.g. **Can you imagine a rabbit hole so deep that you need a rope to get up the slope!**

_____

_____

_____

More spelling patterns

Can you spot the spelling patterns in the words below?

June   rule   rude   cute

tube   tune   cube

fume   glue   use

That's right the vowels go **u** then **e**!

Do you sound out the **e** when you say the words?
No, but it does change how we pronounce the **u** –
it sounds more like **oo**.
Make up a silly sentence for this set of words.

_____

_____

_____

Reward
sticker!

Words with 'ar' and 'ee'

Choose which letters complete each word – **ar** or **ee**?

| ar | ee |

st____   g____den   sh____p

asl____p   c____   h____p

p____k   b____

Words with 'ea'

Some words are spelled with **ea**, but sound like **ee**.
Which ones are correct? Put a circle around them.

dream   cheet

heet
        each   dreem

                              eech
        eet   heat
                                  neat
eat   cheat
          neet

Other words are spelled with **ea**, but sound like **e**.
Which ones are correct? Put a ring around them.

head   heavy

        stedy
                                insted
steady
                hed

instead   hevy

                def

    deaf

Reward
sticker!

Words with 'er'

Complete the crossword below. Here's a clue - it only contains **er** words!

1. Not sweet, it's bitt__

2. Season after spring

3. Not over but und__

4.→ The coldest season

4.↓ When it's not so cold

5. Opposite of brother

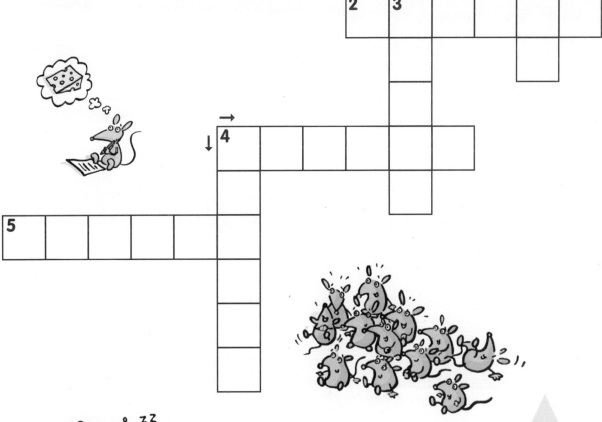

Reward sticker!

19

Scramble mania!

Some words have the same sound when we say them but are spelt differently. Words with **ir** and **ur** are like this. Unscramble the words below.

irbd _ _ _ _

trihs _ _ _ _ _

lirg _ _ _ _

ridht _ _ _ _ _

Reward sticker!

surne _ _ _ _ _

arihc _ _ _ _ _

rulcs _ _ _ _ _

urnb _ _ _ _

aarlipen _ _ _ _ _ _ _ _

Reward sticker!

On the right road

All of the words below have **oa** in the middle. Complete the words and then draw a line to the matching picture.

b____t

t____st

g____l

r____d

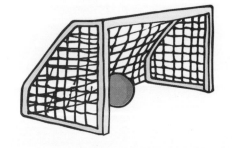

c____ch

Reward sticker!

Words with 'ew' and 'ue'

Words with 'ew' and 'ue' sound the same but are spelt differently. Look at the words below and write them in the correct box.

grew   Tuesday

glue

cue   flew

new   tissue

crew   true   blue

ew	ue

Words with 'ou' and 'ow'

Fill in the missing letters of these **ow** words.

c___   sn___   b___

fl___er   t___n   cr___n

Now see if you can unscramble these words: they are all **ou** words.

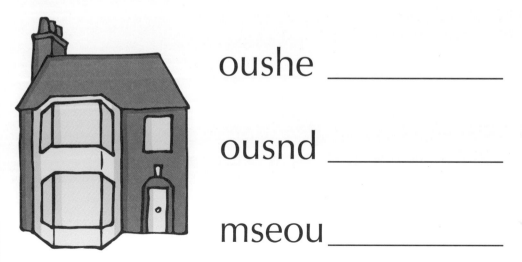

oushe _____

ousnd _____

mseou _____

Reward
sticker!

Words ending in 'y'

All of these words end in **y**.
Using the picture clues, write the missing letters.

__ __ __ __ y

__ __ y

__ __ __ __ __ y

__ __ __ y

__ __ __ __ y

__ __ y

Whales and dolphins

ph can sound a bit like **f** when spelling – don't fall into this trap!
Look at these words and cross out the incorrect spellings.

dolphin   dolfin

elefant   elephant

alphabet   alfabet

phone   fone

wh can be tricky too because you don't always hear the **h**.
Write the **wh** words next to the pictures.

wh __ __ __

wh __ __ __

wh __ __

Reward
sticker!

ie or igh?

ie and igh sound the same. One way to remember which way to spell a word with this sound is that 3 letter words end in ie.
e.g: lie, tie, pie and die.
Longer words tend use igh
e.g: sigh, light, right and fright.

Have a go at this crossword.

1. My kite flew…

2. Opposite of day

3. Don't turn left, turn…

4. Something you turn on to see

5. My tie is too…

6. The spider gave me a…

Reward sticker!

Prefix -un

A prefix is a set of letters we put before a word (this word is known as the root word). Adding a prefix changes the meaning of a word. For example if you add **un**, **seen** becomes **unseen**. **Seen** is the **root word**. Add **un** to the words below.

_____happy

_____do

_____load

_____fair

_____lock

Now look at these words.
What were the root words before **un** was added?
Write them below.

undone _____

unable _____

unfit _____

unkind _____

unzip _____

Reward sticker!

Balloon words

Fill the balloon with as many words as you can with the sound **oo** in them. 10 is good, 15 is brilliant and over 20 is out of this world! Here's one to start you off:

moon

Reward sticker!

Compound words

Compound words are two words joined together to make a new word. For example, farm + yard = farmyard.
Draw a line to connect the words that make up a compound word.

foot	pot
play	work
tea	ball
hand	brush
sea	room
home	chair
tooth	side
arm	bag

Contractions

We use something called an **apostrophe** to shorten words.

Here it is:

The apostrophe takes the place of the missing letter/letters. Look at the examples below and circle the letters that have been missed out.

e.g. can not ➔ can't

should not ➔ shouldn't

was not ➔ wasn't

I would ➔ I'd

you are ➔ you're

you have ➔ you've

shall not ➔ shan't

did not ➔ didn't

I am ➔ I'm

Reward sticker!

Answers

CVC words
cat, bed, fan, cow, dog, hen, nut

Which vowels are missing?
king, flag, bird, frog, drum, ship, harp, mast, swim

'ch', 'sh', 'th' and 'wh' words
ch- chop, chip
sh- shell, wish, fish
th- moth, thin, with
wh- when
shape, wash, church, wish or with, much or mush, which

Ending in 'll', 'ss', 'ff', 'zz' and 'ck'
shell, moss or mock, sock, dull or duff or duck, bell, bull or buzz or buck or buff, fill or fizz

ss- moss, pass
ll- ball, shall,
zz- fizz, buzz
ck- block, muck
ff- fluff

Thinking of fishing
-ng thing, sing, along
-nk link, plank, sprinkle, clunk
b. slick

Words ending in 'tch' and 've'
-tch stopwatch, hatch, witch, catch
-ve glove, hive, live

Words ending in 's' and 'es'
1 clap cats, thanks, spends, rocks, lamps, bags, balls, dogs
2 claps foxes, hatches, witches, catches, matches, boxes

Comparisons
fast, faster, fastest
tall, taller, tallest
low, lower, lowest
kind, kinder, kindest
grand, grander, grandest

Words ending in 'er' and 'est'
-er slower, quicker, hunter, lower, player, older, harder, flower, stronger, shower

-est slowest, quickest, lowest, oldest, hardest, strongest
both slow, quick, low, old, hard, strong

Words ending in 'ay' and 'oy'
may, stray, stay, lay, ray, tray, way, yay, boy, toy, joy, coy.
Did you find anymore?

c	l	s	p	x	v	g	t	f
s	a	t	y	p	m	e	f	t
t	y	r	a	v	a	t	x	o
a	l	a	w	k	y	r	m	y
y	z	y	z	w	f	a	a	g
s	t	b	y	h	k	y	f	s
u	y	c	o	y	s	b	h	j
h	z	a	b	j	o	y	n	e
t	e	b	d	h	w	t	n	v

You're the teacher!
correct rain, wait, train, afraid, fail, tail
incorrect oyl, spoyl, joyn, poynt, soyl, boyl

Five alive

x	n	y	l	i	k	e	m	x	x
h	i	j	g	r	d	k	j	s	t
p	n	b	l	i	s	a	h	e	i
a	e	m	i	d	i	c	i	o	m
l	y	f	n	e	d	w	d	h	e
i	l	i	e	s	t	r	e	t	h
f	i	v	d	s	i	d	e	u	e
e	k	e	a	m	r	s	w	d	k
l	i	n	m	h	i	k	e	b	i
x	q	m	y	x	y	b	o	i	k

Words with 'ar' and 'ee' star, garden, sheep, asleep, car, harp, park, bee

Words with 'ea'
dream, each, heat, neat, eat, cheat, head, heavy, steady, instead, deaf

Words with 'er'
1. bitter, 2. summer, 3. under, 4. → winter, 4. ↓warmer, 5. sister

Scramble mania!
bird, shirt, girl, third, nurse, chair, curls, burn, airplane

On the right road
boat, toast, goal, road, coach

Words with 'ew' and 'ue'
-ew grew, new, flew, crew
-ue glue, Tuesday, cue, tissue, true, blue

Words with 'ou' and 'ow'
cow, snow, bow, flower, town, crown, house, sound, mouse

Words ending in 'y'
lorry, fly, party, baby, family, spy

Whales and dolphins
Correct spellings are: dolphin, elephant, alphabet, phone. wheel, whale, whip

ie or igh?
1. high, 2. night, 3. right, 4. light, 5. tight, 6. fright

Prefix -un
unhappy, undo, unload, unfit, unlock
done, able, fit, kind, zip

Balloon words
food, mood, good, roof, proof, cool, tool, boom, gloom, spoon, soon, scoop, hoot, moor, pool
Did you find anymore **oo** words?

Compound words
football, playroom, teapot, handbag, seaside, homework, toothbrush, armchair

Contractions
should not
was not
I would
you are
you have
shall not
did not
I am

32